PIZZA
IN HIS POCKET
Learning to be Thankful to Allah

JAWAAD ABDUL RAHMAN

ILLUSTRATED BY ACHLA ANAND & ACHAL K. ANAND

Goodword Books Pvt. Ltd.
1, Nizamuddin West Market
New Delhi-110 013
Tel. 435 6666, 435 5454
Fax 9111-435 7333, 435 7980
e-mail: info@goodwordbooks.com
Website: www.goodwordbooks.com

Astrolabe islamicmedia

Goodwordkidz

Helping you build a family of faith

First published 2003
© Goodword Books 2003

Did you ever hear about the boy

Who ate and ate and ate!

He ate early in the morning.
And he ate when it was late.

But he didn't thank Allah for all the yummy food he had.
And he ate so much it made him sick!
Which really made him sad.

He ate hamburgers in Hamburg, which he thought were very nice.
And hot samosas in Sumatra, seasoned with a special spice.

He had tacos in Tijuana with some sauce he got from Spain
And a bowl of fresh bakalava that he bartered in Bahrain.

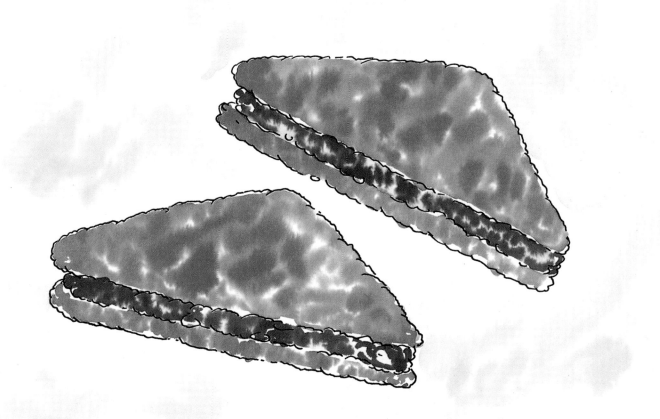

He said gyros made in Cairo are a taste that can't be beat,
and the lemonade in Yemen is a very special treat.

But the turkey made in Turkey
could still use a pinch of salt.
If you ever visit Malta, you should
have a chocolate malt!

He had pizza in his pocket, he had ketchup on his shirt,
And he bought an ice cream sundae, so he wouldn't miss dessert.

On a bay in the Bahamas,
he ate bon-bons in a bunch.
And then he rushed back
home so he could make it
just in time for lunch!

17

Then one day he saw a little girl, who held her tummy tight,
And he walked over and asked her if everything was all right.

She said she was so hungry and had been hungry for so long,
Then he realized the way he ate was very very wrong.

He looked down at his own tummy and he started feeling pain—
Pain from eating too much food, but he knew not to complain.
So he brought the girl some food and shared it with her family,
Then they thanked Allah for what they had, and then he let them be.

So let's try to learn a lesson and let's try to do what's right.
Eat the food your parents give you without a fuss or fight.

And always be thankful to Allah for all your yummy food,
And share what you have with others, because not sharing is rude.

Being thankful is what's really great.
Eat the veggies on your plate.

And don't be like the boy who always ate and ate and ate!

Printed in India by NMIPL